THE KIDS' BOOK OF 18 AWESOME ACTIVITIES

By
Tony Tallarico

Kidsbooks
Incorporated

Hours of challenging fun and games are in store
for you in

THE KIDS' BOOK
OF AWESOME ACTVITIES

Each book is chock full of secret codes, mazes, hidden picture puzzles, word finds, riddles, crosswords, things to draw, and many other zany activities. There's never a dull moment, so get ready to have a blast as you test your skills trying to solve these awesome puzzles.

What are you waiting for? Sharpen your pencil and let's go!

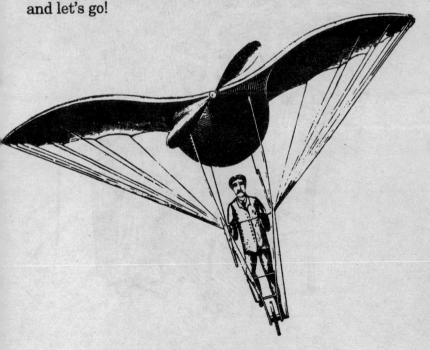

Answers begin on page 156.

SPOT A PIX

FIND **10** THINGS THAT ARE DIFFERENT BETWEEN THESE TWO PICTURES.

WORD FIND

Find and circle these words about the MORNING.
They go up, down, forward, backward,
and diagonally.

ALARM	LATE
AWAKE	MILK
BREAKFAST	NEWS
CEREAL	RADIO
COMB	RUSH
COOK	SHOWER
DASH	SOAP
DRESS	TIRED
EGGS	TOAST
HURRY	WASH
JUICE	WATER
KITCHEN	YAWN

M Y K D J U I C E
V H W N O I D A R
H S A W A T E R T
T N W A Y R R U H
S N E H C T I K S
A L A R M S T L U
F A C W H S S I R
K E S O A P G M S
A R W O M K G S Q
E E T A L B E W J
R C O O K R J E Z
B H S A D B T N T

7

WHAT DO YOU GET IF YOU CROSS A SKUNK WITH A BEE?

USE THIS CHART TO DECODE THE ANSWER.

SUN	MON	TUES	WED	THURS	FRI	SAT
1 J	2 E	3 P	4 S	5 I	6 T	7 F
8 B	9 Q	10 U	11 A	12 X	13 H	14 Z
15 V	16 M	17 G	18 Y	19 O	20 L	21 R
22 N	23 K	24 D	25 W	26 C		

WED 11   SUN 22   WED 11   SUN 22   THURS 5   MON 16   WED 11   FRI 20

FRI 6   FRI 13   WED 11   FRI 6

WED 4   FRI 6   THURS 5   SUN 22   MON 23   WED 4   WED 11   SUN 22   TUES 24

WED 4   FRI 6   THURS 5   SUN 22   TUES 17   WED 4   !

GO FOR IT

CAN YOU FIND YOUR WAY TO THE
EASTER BASKET?

A-MAZE-ING!

DECODE

DECODE THE MESSAGE
USING THIS CHART.

A	B	C	D	E	F	G	H	I	J	K	L	M
1	2	3	4	5	6	7	8	9	10	11	12	13
N	O	P	Q	R	S	T	U	V	W	X	Y	Z
14	15	16	17	18	19	20	21	22	23	24	25	26

$\overline{}_{4}\ \overline{}_{15}\ \overline{}_{14}\ \overline{}_{20}$

$\overline{}_{2}\ \overline{}_{5}$

$\overline{}_{1}$

$\overline{}_{12}\ \overline{}_{9}\ \overline{}_{20}\ \overline{}_{20}\ \overline{}_{5}\ \overline{}_{18}$

$\overline{}_{2}\ \overline{}_{21}\ \overline{}_{7}$!

CROSSWORD PICTURE FUN

ACROSS:

2. ONE WHO PERFORMS TRICKS

4. PERCUSSION INSTRUMENT

6. YOU LISTEN WITH THESE

8. FAMILY PET

DOWN:

1. USED TO TAKE PHOTOS

3. _ _ _ _ _ SHOWERS BRING MAY FLOWERS

5. STAMPED ENVELOPES

7. KITCHEN UTENSIL

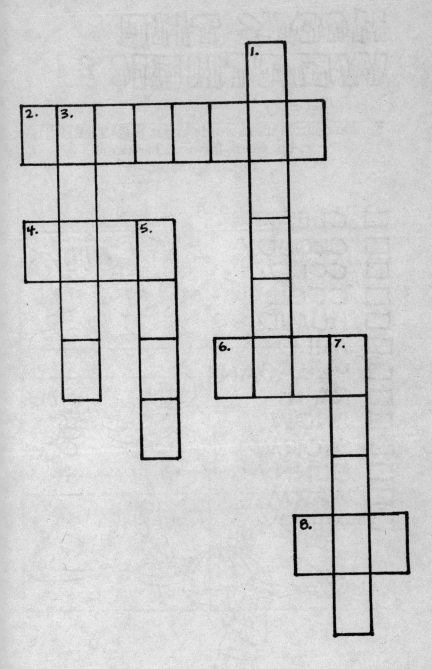

HOW'S THE WEATHER?

Find and circle these words about **WEATHER**. They go up, down, forward, backward, and diagonally.

- ☐ CLEAR
- ☐ CLOUDY
- ☐ COLD
- ☐ COOL
- ☐ HUMID
- ☐ MILD
- ☐ PLEASANT
- ☐ RAIN
- ☐ SNOW
- ☐ STORM
- ☐ SUNNY
- ☐ WARM
- ☐ WINDY

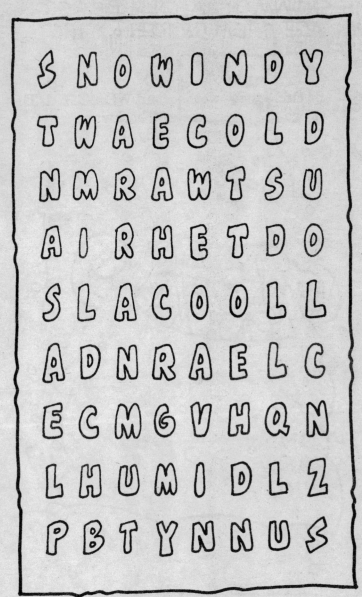

S N O W I N D Y
T W A E C O L D
N M R A W T S U
A I R H E T D O
S L A C O O L L
A D N R A E L C
E C M G V H Q N
L H U M I D L Z
P B T Y N N U S

15

SNOWMAN MATH

THIS SNOWMAN HAS NUMBERS ON HIM. ADD THEM UP TO FIND THE TOTAL.

TOTAL

FIND "B"

CIRCLE THE **8** THINGS IN THIS PICTURE THAT BEGIN WITH THE LETTER "**B**".

TWIN GIRLS

CIRCLE THE TWIN GIRLS.

OLYMPIC FUN

WRITE THESE WORDS HAVING TO DO WITH THE OLYMPIC GAMES IN THE GRID BELOW.

ATHLETES • CYCLE •
GYMNAST • HOCKEY •
MEDALS • SPORTS •
TRIUMPH • WIN •

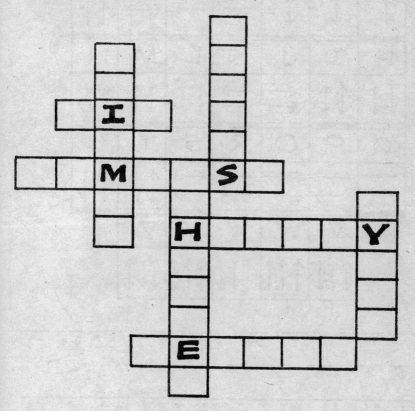

SECRET JOKE

Write the letters that match the code symbols
in the blanks below.

WHY WASN'T CINDERELLA
GOOD AT PLAYING
FOOTBALL?

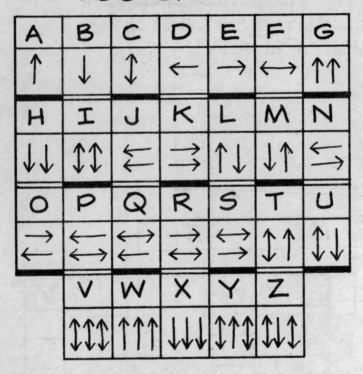

DANCE TO THE MUSIC

WRITE THESE WORDS HAVING TO DO WITH MUSIC IN THE GRID BELOW.

COUNTRY • FEELING • FOLK • HEAVY • MELODY • ROCK • TEMPO • TUNE

USE THIS CHART TO DECODE THE FOLLOWING FACT.

A	B	C	D	E	F	G	H	I	J	K	L	M
20	13	4	22	2	19	26	10	7	23	3	15	5

N	O	P	Q	R	S	T	U	V	W	X	Y	Z
16	9	25	11	8	6	1	17	21	14	18	24	12

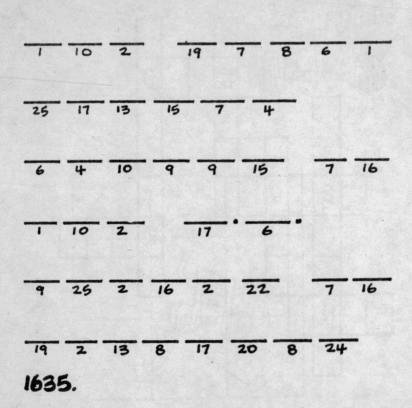

```
__ __ __    __ __ __ __ __
1  10  2    19  7  8  6  1

__ __ __ __ __ __
25 17 13 15  7  4

__ __ __ __ __ __     __ __
6   4  10  9  9  15    7  16

__ __ __    __ . __ ..
1  10  2    17   6

__ __ __ __ __ __    __ __
9  25  2  16  2  22   7  16

__ __ __ __ __ __ __ __
19  2  13  8  17 20  8  24
```

1635.

DOUBLE WORD

ANSWER THESE CLUES AND WRITE THEM IN THEIR CORRECT SPACES. THE ANSWERS WILL READ THE SAME VERTICALLY AS WELL AS HORIZONTALLY.

1- WHAT YOU GET WHEN IT RAINS.

2- FEMALE SHEEP.

3- 6 + 4 = _____ .

	1-	2-	3-
1-			
2-			
3-			

FILL IN

Fill in the areas that contain a dot to read this hidden message.

FIND APPLE

FIND THE WORD **APPLE** WHICH
APPEARS **12** TIMES IN THIS PUZZLE.
CIRCLE THEM.

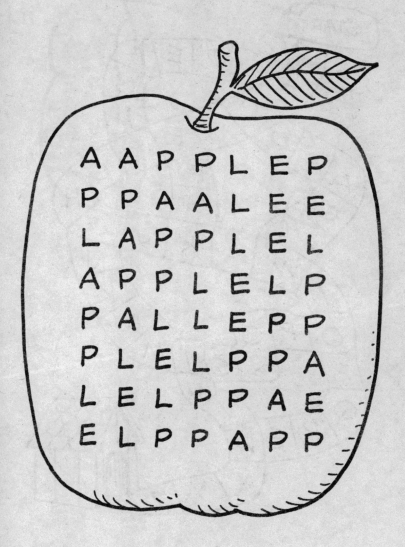

```
A A P P L E P
P P A A L E E
L A P P L E L
A P P L E L P
P A L L E P P
P L E L P P A
L E L P P A E
E L P P A P P
```

MYSTERY PIX

DRAW WHAT YOU SEE FROM THE NUMBERED BOXES ABOVE INTO THE SAME NUMBERED BOXES BELOW.

1	2	3	4
5	**6**	**7**	**8**
9	**10**	**11**	**12**

MAKE WORDS

CAN YOU MAKE AT LEAST
15 WORDS USING THE
LETTERS IN THE WORD
SNOWDRIFT ?

DOT

PENCIL MAZE

Find a path from the eraser to the point.

CROSS OUT

Cross out the letters D, E, H, M, and V. List the remaining letters, in the order they appear, in the blank spaces below.

```
L  O  V  M  O
H  K  E  O  U
D  T  F  O  R
V  S  C  H  M
A  R  Y  V  D
G  O  B  L  H
D  I  N  V  S
```

LOOK OUT FOR SCARY

GOBLINS!

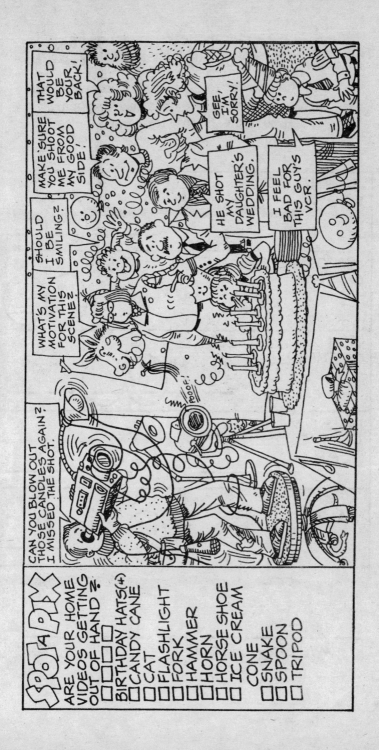

31

THE MYSTERY WORD IS...

Write the answer to each clue. Then write the
circled letters, in the order they appear,
to form the mystery word.

___ AND GO SEEK.

_ _ (_) _

OPPOSITE OF OUT.

(_) (_)

NOT OPENED.

_ _ (_) (_) _ _

FIRST MONTH OF THE YEAR.

_ (_) _ (_) _ _ _

NOT FAKE.

(_) _ _ _ _

_ _ _ _ _ _ _ _ _

MYSTERY WORD

WHAT'Z WRONG?

FIND **6** THINGS WRONG AT THIS FUN FAIR.

CROSSWORD

Help the Magic Egg complete this
crossword puzzle.

across	down
1. JELLY_____	2. YOU COLOR THEM
4. NOT SQUARE	3. EASTER SEASON
6. 8TH MONTH	5. BUNNY _____

CROSS OUT ALL THE
LETTERS THAT APPEAR
3 TIMES.
WRITE THE REMAINING
LETTERS, AS THEY
APPEAR, IN THE BLANK
SPACES BELOW.

C	B	E	L
I	Z	J	N
N	C	Z	E
A	J	N	R
E	D	J	C

_____ _____ _____ _____

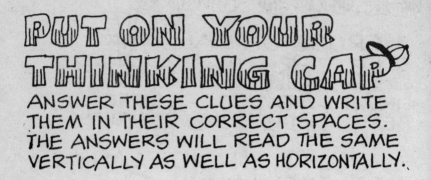

PUT ON YOUR THINKING CAP

ANSWER THESE CLUES AND WRITE
THEM IN THEIR CORRECT SPACES.
THE ANSWERS WILL READ THE SAME
VERTICALLY AS WELL AS HORIZONTALLY.

1. YOU WEAR THIS ON YOUR HEAD.

2. TO MATURE OR GROW.

3. FIVE PLUS FIVE EQUALS____.

	1.	2.	3.
1.			
2.			
3.			

WHAT'S THE DIFFERENCE?

FIND **6** THING THAT ARE DIFFERENT
BETWEEN THESE TWO PICTURES.

WORD FILL

Fill in this word wall by using only the letters
from the top word to complete the words below.
Some letters may be used more than once.

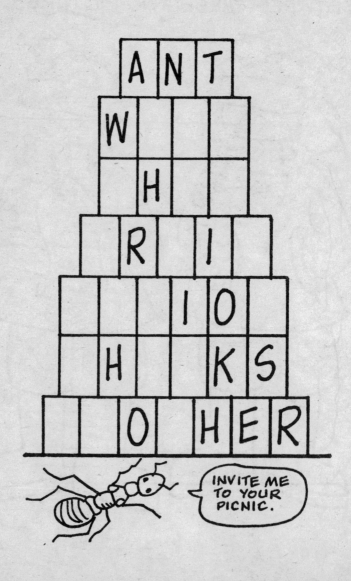

MAZE

Help the earthlings land on planet "Y-ME."

HIDDEN RIDDLE

Use the chart to decode the answer to this riddle. First go across, and then down, to find the correct letters.

WHAT DID THE GRASS SAY TO THE LAWN MOWER ?

	1	2	3	4	5
1	S	R	Y	H	N
2	A	I	T	M	U
3	T	B	W	F	E
4	O	K	R	T	H

23 45 21 15 42 11

34 41 12

31 14 35

44 43 22 24

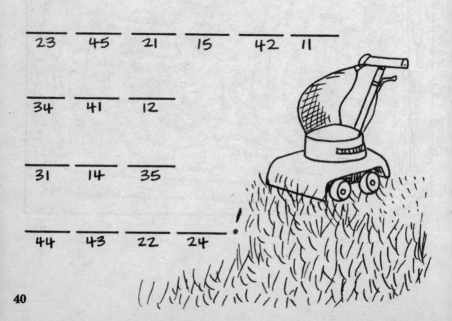

WHAT'S WRONG?

Find at least **6** things wrong here.

MYSTERY PIX

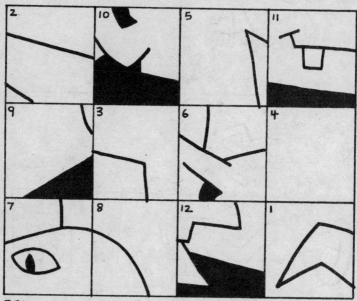

DRAW WHAT YOU SEE FROM THE NUMBERED BOXES
ABOVE INTO THE SAME NUMBERED BOXES BELOW

1	2	3	4
5	6	7	8
9	10	11	12

"TAKE ME TO YOUR LEADER!" MAZE

CIRCLE IT!

CIRCLE THE NAME "PETER" EVERYTIME IT APPEARS IN THE PUZZLE. LIST THE REMAINING LETTERS IN THE SPACES BELOW TO REVEAL THE HIDDEN PHRASE.

```
      B   U   N
  P   P   R   N   P
  E   E   E   Y   E
  T   T   T   T   T
  E   E   E   E   E
  R   R   P   R   R
  R   E   T   E   P
      A   I   L
```

_ _ _ _ _   _ _ _ _ _

CIRCLE ★

CIRCLE ALL THE LETTERS THAT HAVE
A STAR ★ . WRITE THESE LETTERS
BELOW, AS THEY APPEAR, TO MAKE
THE HIDDEN PHRASE.

■ W	★ E	▼ Z	★ A		
★ S	☾ B	▲ C	★ T	▲ B	★ E
● R	★ R	☾ D	▬ B	★ P	◀ R
▮ T	★ A	▲ J	★ R	● R	★ A
	▼ J	★ D	★ E	◀ T	

_ _ _ _ _ _   _ _ _ _ _ _

45

WHO'S COMING?

CIRCLE THE LETTERS THAT CONTAIN A SQUARE □. WRITE THESE LETTERS, AS THEY APPEAR, IN THE BLANK SPACES BELOW.

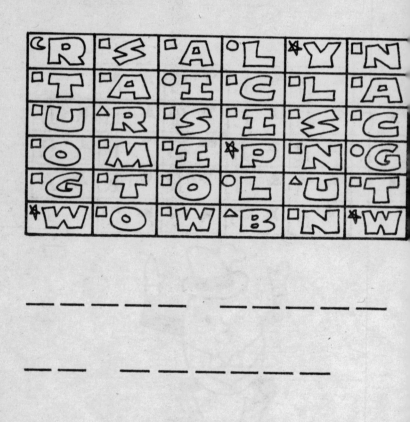

_ _ _ _ _ _ _ _ _

_ _ _ _ _ _ _ _

_ _ _ _ _ _ _ .

MAKE-WORDS Puzzle

Create your own list of words using
the letters from: WELCOME BACK

MAZE...
SNORING ZONE!

WORD FIND

Find and circle these words about the **STATUE OF LIBERTY**. They go up, down, forward, backward, and diagonally.

A—Admire; C—Copper, Cost, Crown; D—Dimensions; E—Ellis Island; F—France, Foundation, Free, Fund; G—Gift, Grant, Great, Greet; H—Harbor, Help, Hope, Hudson; I—Immigrants, Iron; L—Lamp, Large, Liberty Island; M—Mammoth, Miss Liberty, Money; P—Pay, Pedestal, Pride, Project, Pulitzer; S—Spirit, Statue, Steel; T—Tablets, Tall, Torch, Tourists; U—Unique; W—Welcome

```
N D N A L S I S I L L E A M C
O P L E H Y E N O M U E D A R
S U D I P Y E D E Q U H M M O
D L I N M A R N I T C I I M W
U I M T A P F N A R S I R O N
H T E I L L U T O S P S E T O
O Z N R C O S T L A R G E H I
R E S I I M M I G R A N T S T
O R I P R W B T Y G R E A T A
B D O S T E L B A T I T O N D
R N N S R L E C N A R F A A N
A U S T H C O P P E R E T R U
H F Y E T O U R I S T S B G O
G R E E T M P R O J E C T I F
T A L L R E P E D E S T A L L
```

51

HIDDEN PICTURES

FIND: ☐KEY ☐KITE ☐FACE ☐STAR
☐APPLE ☐PEAR ☐HEART ☐PENCIL
☐TOP HAT ☐FISH

FIND: ☐STAR ☐PIG ☐FORK
☐TOOTHBRUSH ☐LOG ☐CAR ☐SANTA
☐EAR ☐EYE ☐BLOCK ☐PIE ☐SAW
☐PIPE

WORD FIND

Find and circle these words having to do with the **CALENDAR**. They go up, down, forward, backward, and diagonally.

A—Appointment, April, August; B—Birthday; C—Conference; D—Date, December; E—Evening, Event; F—Friday; H—Holiday; I—Important; J—January, July, June; M—March, Meeting, Monday, Month, Morning; N—Note, November; O—Occasion, October; P—Party, Place; S—Saturday, Schedule, September, Sunday; T—Thursday, Time, Tuesday; V—Vacation; W—Wednesday, Week

```
F R I D A Y A D H T R I B K A
W E D N E S D A Y M N T H E J
E T N E M T N I O P P A T E A
M O T N A T R O P M I Y N W N
I N S N O I S A C C O A O C U
T S A L I R P A Y T J D M O A
O C T O B E R A U G U S T N R
G H U E T A D E R G N R M F Y
N E R E E N S E B T E U A E A
I D D E U D T J C M Y H R R D
T U A S A G N N U E E T C E I
E L Y Y P L A C E L M T H N L
E E N O I T A C A V Y B P C O
M O R N I N G N I N E V E E H
Y A D N O M N O V E M B E R S
```

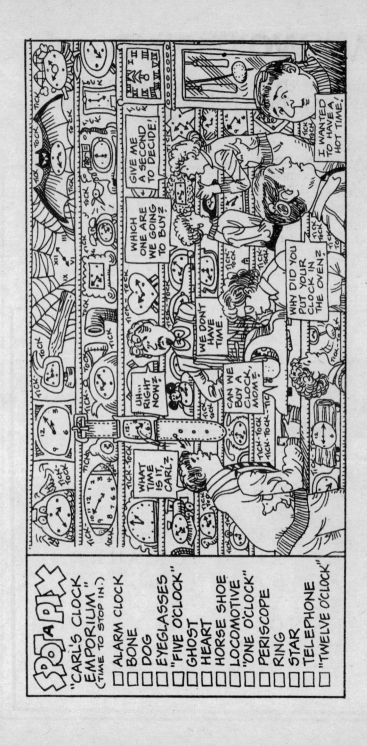

55

MAKE-WORDS Puzzle

Create your list of words
using the letters from:
SUPERCALIFRAGILISTIC

WORD FIND

Find and circle these words about **BUILDING A HOUSE**. They go up, down, forward, backwards, and diagonally.

A—Attic   B—Basement, Brick, Budget, Build
C—Carpenter, Cement, Chimney, Closets, Concrete, Construct, Cost   D—Deck   F—Floor, Frame
G—Girder   H—Home   K—Kitchen   L—Land, Location, Lumber   M—Money   N—Nails   O—Owner
P—Paint, Pipes, Plan, Plaster, Porch   R—Roof, Rooms   S—Shingle, Size, Solid, Space, Stairs, Style, Supplies   T—Tools   V-Vent   W—Wallboard, Windows, Wood, Work

```
S R K A H M N P L A S T E R U
T E C N O R O A E C A P S E K
E T E T M O I I Z B U I L D R
S N D V E N T N I F L O O R O
O E I S R I A T S W O D N I W
L P L A N K C R E B M U L G A
C R O Y C I O H O S L I A N L
O A S I T O L B I O L I N C L
N C R T M S N T F M F O D O B
S B A S E M E N T N N O O S O
T E G D U B H E P I P E S T A
R O W N E R C M O N E Y Y D R
U E M A R F T E L G N I H S D
C P O R C H I C O N C R E T E
T O D O O W K S E I L P P U S
```

MAZE STRIKE!

GO FOR A STRIKE.

HIDDEN RIDDLE

USE THIS CHART TO DECODE THE ANSWER

WHAT KIND OF TICKLE ISN'T FUNNY ?

A	B	C	D	E	F	G	H	I
>	<	+	÷	=	–	X	><	>+

J	K	L	M	N	O	P	Q	R
)÷	>=	>–	>X	<>	<+	<÷	<=	<–

S	T	U	V	W	X	Y	Z
<x	+>	+<	++	+÷	+=	+–	+x

>   +>   >+   +   >=   >–   =

>+   <>   +–   <+   +<   <–

+>   ><   <–   <+   >   +> !

MATCH!

WHICH ONE OF THESE FIRE FIGHTERS
IS DIFFERENT FROM THE REST?
LOOK CAREFULLY.

WHAT'S GOING ON?
FIND AND CIRCLE **10** THINGS THAT ARE WRONG IN THIS PICTURE.

CROSS OUT THE LETTERS
THAT HAVE A BOX □.
WRITE THE REMAINING
LETTERS, AS THEY
APPEAR, TO REVEAL THE
NAME OF A HOLIDAY.

△ T	□ E	✶ H	○ A	□ F
□ N	○ N	△ K	□ Y	□ C
✶ S	□ A	□ N	○ G	□ T
□ S	△ I	□ T	✶ V	○ I
✶ N	□ E	△ G	□ U	□ W

_ _ _ _ _ _ _ _ _ _ _ _

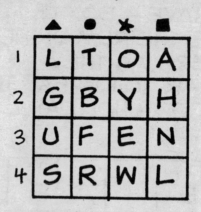

MORE TO DECODE

USE THIS CHART TO DECODE THIS BASEBALL FACT.

BASEBALL GREAT BABE RUTH WAS BORN FEBRUARY 6, 1895.

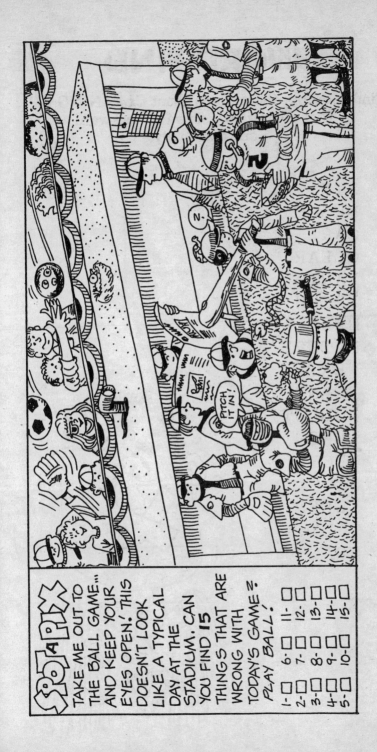

WORD FIND

Find and circle these words about **CLEANING UP**.
They go up, down, forward, backward,
and diagonally.

AIR
BROOM
CARE
CLEAR
EARTH
FRESH
HELP
NATURE
NEAT
PLANT
POLLUTION
PURE
RECYCLE
SMOG
SWEEP
TIDY
TRASH

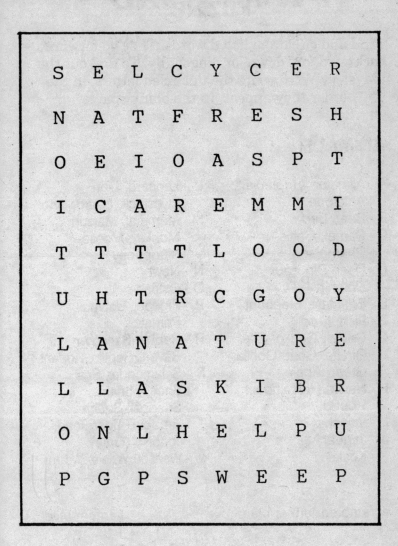

```
S  E  L  C  Y  C  E  R
N  A  T  F  R  E  S  H
O  E  I  O  A  S  P  T
I  C  A  R  E  M  M  I
T  T  T  T  L  O  O  D
U  H  T  R  C  G  O  Y
L  A  N  A  T  U  R  E
L  L  A  S  K  I  B  R
O  N  L  H  E  L  P  U
P  G  P  S  W  E  E  P
```

YOU CAN PREVENT NOISE POLLUTION

... _ _ _ _   _ _ _ _ _ _ !

Mystery Word-Search Puzzle

Find and circle the listed words. They go forward, backward, up, down, or diagonally. To find out the Mystery Word write the uncircled letters, in the order they appear, in the blank spaces.

ANIMALS

A - Alligator, Amphibian, Antelope
B - Bear, Bird
C - Camel, Cattle, Chameleon
D - Deer, Dinosaur, Dolphin
E - Edentate, Elephant
F - Fish, Frog
G - Gavial, Gecko, Gila, Giraffe, Goat, Gorilla, Green Anole
H - Hawk, Hellbender, Hound
I - Insect
J - Jaguar
K - Koala

L - Leopard, Lion, Livestock, Lizard, Lynx
M - Mammal, Marsupial, Monkey, Moose, Mudpuppy
N - Newt
O - Ostrich
P - Pigeon, Platypus, Primate
R - Rabbit, Raccoon, Raven, Reptile, Rodent
S - Salamander, Seal, Sheep, Snake, Snapper, Squirrel
T - Terrapin, Tiger, Toad, Tortoise, Turtle
W - Weasel, Whale, Worm

scrambled letters clue: Large reptile.

_____

mystery word:

_____

```
L E R R I U Q S U P Y T A L P
W H A L E L T T A C I L E E R
E H N S N A K E L S L G L S A
A E T R O M O E A I O I E O V
S L E E O M M L G R Z N P O E
E L L P C A A A I A O S H M N
L B O P C M T L R I B E A R A
E E P A A O L D L G M C N U M
O N E N R A E L T R U T T A P
P D D S R E G I T E D N E S H
A E E T A T N E D E P I T O I
R R H C I R T S O N U P A N B
D R H S I F R O G A P A M I I
L O A L A I V A G N P R I D A
A D L B P E E H S O Y R R G N
I E A P B D X N Y L A E P I Y
P N O O H I L I R E P T I L E
U T K R T I T R A U G A J A K
S O K C E G N R E E D R I B N
R C H A M E L E O N K W A H O
A E K C O T S E V I L A E S M
M R O W N E W T O R T O I S E
C C D N U O H E F F A R I G O
```

BOWLING MAZE

TRAVEL THROUGH THE CORRECT
MAZE PATH TO BOWL A STRIKE.

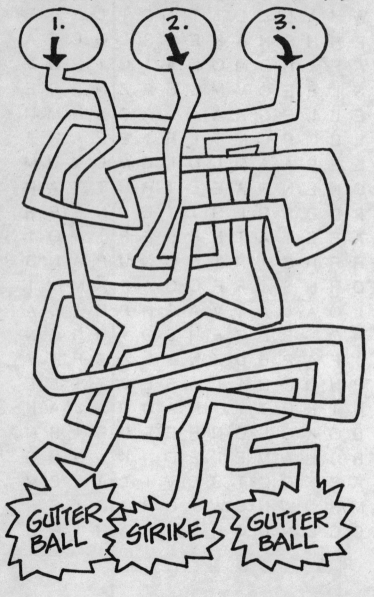

USNCRMABLE

U.S. PRESIDENTS.

18TH PRESIDENT

ULYSSES S.

TNARG

_____

32ND PRESIDENT

FRANKLIN D.

OROSEVTLE

_____

FILL-IN MAZE

FILL IN THE AREAS THAT HAVE A DOT
TO FIND THE PATH THAT LEADS TO THE
MOON.

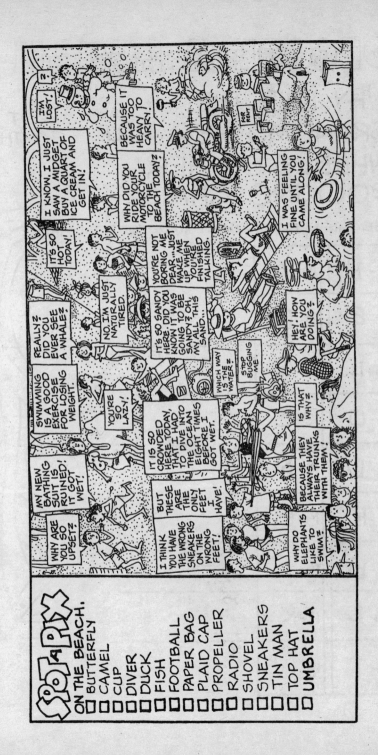

75

WHY DID THE GRANDMOTHER PUT WHEELS ON HER ROCKING CHAIR?

USE THIS SPECIAL CHART TO DECODE THE ANSWER.

1– H	10– A
2– E	11– D
3– L	12– O
4– U	13– C
5– D	14– N
6– R	15– E
7– B	16– S
8– L	17– K
9– T	18– W

$\overline{7}\ \overline{2}\ \overline{13}\ \overline{10}\ \overline{4}\ \overline{16}\ \overline{2}$

$\overline{16}\ \overline{1}\ \overline{15}$

$\overline{18}\ \overline{10}\ \overline{14}\ \overline{9}\ \overline{2}\ \overline{5}$

$\overline{9}\ \overline{12}$

$\overline{6}\ \overline{12}\ \overline{13}\ \overline{17}$

$\overline{10}\ \overline{14}\ \overline{11}$

$\overline{6}\ \overline{12}\ \overline{3}\ \overline{8}$!

A-MAZE-ING!

MAKE-WORDS Puzzle

Create your own list of words using
the letters from: **SPIDERWEB**

VALENTINE PUZZLE

THE NAME **CUPID** APPEARS IN THIS PUZZLE **8** TIMES. FIND AND CIRCLE EACH ONE.

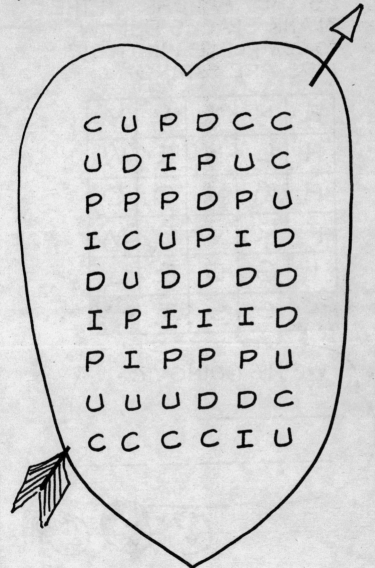

C U P D C C
U D I P U C
P P P D P U
I C U P I D
D U D D D D
I P I I I D
P I P P P U
U U U D D C
C C C C I U

CIRCLE THEM!

CIRCLE EVERY 3RD LETTER. WRITE THESE, AS THEY APPEAR, IN THE BLANK SPACES BELOW TO COMPLETE WHAT THE KIDS ARE SAYING.

E	N	T	V	Y
H	L	K	E	W
H	M	N	O	O
F	R	V	S	M
I	G	D	E	L
	S	S	T	

WE'RE GOING TO
_____ _____ !

WHAT'S WRONG ?

Find at least **8** things wrong here.

81

MYSTERY NAME

WRITE THE ANSWER TO EACH CLUE IN THE SPACES TO THE RIGHT. THEN LIST THE CIRCLED LETTERS, IN THE ORDER THAT THEY APPEAR, TO FORM THE MYSTERY NAME.

OPPOSITE OF
FIRST

◯ — — —

YOU HAVE 5 OF THESE ON
EACH HAND

— ◯◯ — — —

FROZEN
WATER

— ◯ —

HALLOWEEN
MONTH

◯ — — — — —

YELLOW CITRUS
FRUIT

◯ — — — ◯

— — — — — — — —
MYSTERY NAME

82

LOOK AND FIND

FIND AND CIRCLE THESE
HIDDEN OBJECTS:
☐ARROW ☐BALLOON ☐COMB
☐DRUM ☐KEY ☐RING ☐STAR
☐TELESCOPE

DRINK-UP MAZE

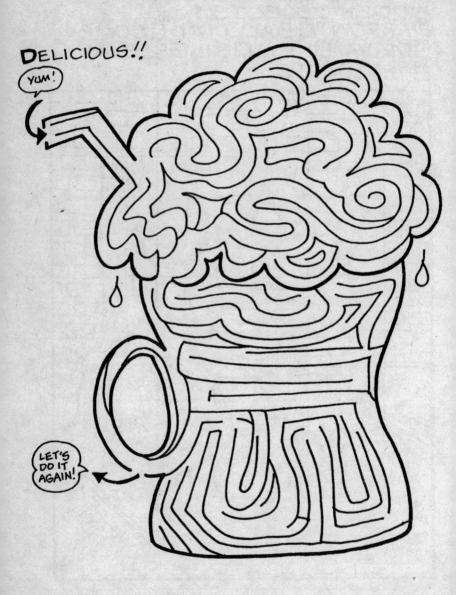

CIRCLE ☆

CIRCLE THE LETTERS THAT CONTAIN A STAR ☆.   WRITE THESE LETTERS, AS THEY APPEAR, TO REVEAL THE MYSTERY MESSAGE.

L ▷	H ☆	N △	A ☆
P ☆	Q ○	P ☆	S ▢
O ☽	R ◁	P ▽	Y ☆
H ☆	O ☆	T ☽	X ◁
V ▢	L ☆	W ▭	I ☆
D ☆	V ☽	A ☆	F △
M ▽	Y ☆	S ☆	B ▽

— — — — —

— — — — — — — — !

THE MYSTERY WORD IS...

WRITE THE ANSWER TO EACH CLUE. THEN WRITE THE CIRCLED LETTERS, IN THE ORDER THAT THEY APPEAR, TO FORM THE MYSTERY WORD.

OPPOSITE
OF HOT – ◯ ◯ __ __

THIRD MONTH
OF THE YEAR – ◯ __ __ __ __

SMALL POOLE
OF RAIN – ◯ ◯ __ __ __

THIRD DAY OF
THE WEEK – ◯ __ ◯ __ __ __

NOT SQUARE – ◯ __ __ __ __

__ __ __ __ __ __ __ __ __

MYSTERY WORD

MISSING VOWELS

THESE WORDS ARE MISSING THEIR VOWELS **A • E • I • O • U**. WRITE THE CORRECT VOWELS IN THE RIGHT SPACES. THE CLUE WILL HELP YOU.

Word	Clue
_ P _ N	(NOT CLOSED)
_ PPL _	(A JUICY RED FRUIT)
SH _ _	(YOU WEAR THIS ON YOUR FOOT)
_ MBR _ LL _	(OPEN THIS UP WHEN IT RAINS)
W _ NT _ R	(DECEMBER TO MARCH)
P _ _ N _	(EIGHTY-EIGHT KEYS)
N _ V _ MB _ R	(THANKSGIVING MONTH)

LOOK FOR...

THE WORD "SNOWMAN." IT APPEARS **7** TIMES IN THIS PUZZLE. FIND AND CIRCLE EACH ONE.

```
S N O W M A N S
N A M W O N S N
O O N M S N N N
W M A N M A O A
M A M N M S W M
A A W O N M W
N N O W M A A O
S N N O W W N N
S S S S N N S S
```

THIS WORD WHEEL CAN SPELL A HIDDEN MESSAGE. STARTING WITH THE NUMBER **1**, GO TWICE AROUND THE CIRCLE CLOCKWISE, AND WRITE EVERY OTHER LETTER IN THE BLANK SPACES.

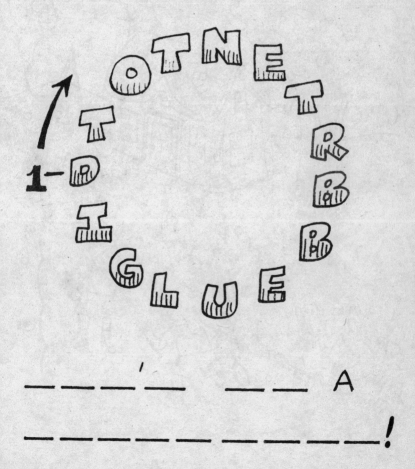

1—

D O N ' T   B E   A

L I T T E R B U G !

IN SEARCH OF...

FIND THE FOLLOWING LETTERS
AND NUMBERS IN THIS SCENE.

A · B · C · D · E · F
1 · 2 · 3 · 4 · 5 · 6

SCRAMBLED WORDS

UNSCRAMBLE THESE WORDS HAVING TO DO WITH VALENTINE'S DAY.

1. ETHRA

   _ _ A _ _

2. EOVL

   L _ _ _

3. CPDUI

   _ _ _ _ D

4. KSIS

   _ _ S _

5. FEOWLSR

   _ _ _ W _ _ _

6. VGIE

   _ I _ _

LOOK ALIKE

THESE TWO PICTURES OF SANTA ARE
ALMOST ALIKE. CAN YOU FIND **6**
THINGS THAT ARE DIFFERENT
BETWEEN THEM?

HOW MANY?

HOW MANY TIMES DOES THE WORD BUNNY APPEAR? CIRCLE AND COUNT EACH.

SUMMIT MAZE

Help the hiker find the right path down
the mountain.

WORD FIND

Find and circle these words about **ECOLOGY**. They go up, down, forward, backward, and diagonally.

A—Air **B**—Balance **C**—Care, Community, Crime **D**—Dams, Drainage, Dry **E**—Erosion **F**—Flood, Food, Forest **G**—Good **H**—Health, Humus **I**— Influence **L**—Land, Lumber **M**—Medicine, Mineral **N**—Natural, Nutrition **P**—Peace, Population **Q**—Quantity **R**—Resources, Runoff **S**—Sewage, Shelter, Soil, Solution, Store, Supply **T**—Trees **U**—Useful **W**—Waste, Water, Wildlife, Wind, Wise, World

```
S U P P L Y T I N U M M O C P
H E A L T H W A T E R E T R O
E E G A N I A R D R S T S I P
L E F I L D L I W O O S E M U
T R W A M C C O W S I A R E L
E O I I A I R I D I L W O C A
R T S R N L N O D O O L F A T
R S E E D D O E E N Y R D E I
B E U S E F U L R P C O O P O
A W F O L A R U T A N T O S N
L A F U A R E B M U L T G E H
A G O R N U T R I T I O N E U
N E N C D Y T I T N A U Q R M
C O U E C N E U L F N I I T U
E N R S O L U T I O N D A M S
```

Mystery Word-Search Puzzle

Find and circle the listed words. They go forward, backward, up, down, or diagonally.

TOYLAND

A - Arcade
B - Ball, Blocks, Bubbles
C - Checkers, Children, Clay, Coloring book, Comic book, Costume, Crayons
D - Doll, Dominoes, Drum
E - Easel
F - Frisbee
G - Games, Go-cart
H - Horn, Hula-Hoop
J - Jacks, Jump rope
K - Kaleidoscope, Kids, Kite
M - Magic, Marbles, Mask, Music box

P - Paint, Piggy bank, Ping-Pong, Pinwheel, Playpen, Plaything, Puppet, Puzzle
R - Rattle, Rocking horse, Roller skates, Rubber duck
S - Seesaw, Sled, Smile, Soccer, Swing set
T - Teddy bear, Teeter totter, Toys, Trains, Tricycle, Truck
W - Wagon, Whistle
Y - Yo-yo

To find out the Mystery Word write the uncircled letters, in the order they appear, in the blank spaces.

Scrambled letters clue: Fun on wheels

_____

mystery word:

_____

```
D S E T A K S R E L L O R O R
E T B E S R O H G N I K C O R
L K A K A L E I D O S C O P E
S M I L E S D I K K C U R T L
L M A G I C E L C Y C I R T T
L S N O Y A R C U S N I A R T
O G E S K C A J D L E S A E A
D N C H E C K E R S O C C E R
R I H U L L A B E M U T S O C
E H I L T P B M B E L Z Z U P
T T L A S I A B B P A I N T A
T Y D H I G T P U P P E T R K
O A R O H G E L R B L O C K S
T L E O W Y S E L B R A M C A
R P N P A B G E S T D U L K M
E T I K G A N H E E R A F O X
T O Y S O N I W O D Y T R O O
E H O R N K W N N D A R I B B
E W A S E E S I I Y O A S C C
T N E P Y A L P M B Y C B I I
G N O P G N I P O E O O E M S
E P O R P M U J D A Y G E O U
S D K O O B G N I R O L O C M
```

CIRCLE IT!

Circle the following objects that are
hidden in Santa's Workshop.

**TOOTHBRUSH SPOON FOOTBALL DRUM
CAMERA HEART BROOM EYEGLASSES**

MAZE TRIP

Correctly travel through this maze to reach
the pine tree.

Circle all the letters that have a triangle.
Write these letters, in the order they appear,
to form the mystery word below.

○ C	△ J	□ L	△ E
△ L	△ L	☾ H	▭ S
☾ L	○ R	△ Y	△ B
△ E	△ A	□ Z	☆ E
☆ M	△ N	☽ T	△ S

_ _ _ _ _ _ _ _ _ _

DECODE

USE THIS CHART TO DECODE THE MESSAGE.

A	B	C	D	E	F	G	H	I	J	K	L	M
6	9	22	20	23	1	16	19	2	11	25	13	17

N	O	P	Q	R	S	T	U	V	W	X	Y	Z
5	7	24	12	26	8	4	3	14	21	18	10	15

I T S '
2 4 8

F U N
1 3 5

T O
4 7

B U I L D
9 3 2 13 20

C A S T L E S
22 6 8 4 13 23 8

I N
2 5

T H E
4 19 23

S N O W .
8 5 7 21

HOOP MAZE

SHOOT A THREE-POINT
BASKET !

CASTLE SEARCH

CAN YOU FIND AND CIRCLE THE
FOLLOWING HIDDEN OBJECTS IN THIS
CASTLE?

BIRD KEY GHOST SHOE PUMPKIN
BROOM COBWEB STAR CANDLE

ACROSS THE U.S.A.

FIND AND CIRCLE THE NAMES OF THESE U.S. STATES AND CITIES:

- ☐ ARIZONA
- ☐ ATLANTA
- ☐ BOSTON
- ☐ DALLAS
- ☐ DETROIT
- ☐ IDAHO
- ☐ IOWA
- ☐ KANSAS
- ☐ MAINE
- ☐ MIAMI
- ☐ NEW JERSEY
- ☐ NEW YORK
- ☐ OHIO
- ☐ SAN DIEGO
- ☐ TEXAS
- ☐ TOLEDO
- ☐ TULSA
- ☐ UTAH
- ☐ VIRGINIA
- ☐ WACO

```
Y E S R E J W E N B
T D R M O D E L O T
O H D A L L A S T O
I M A I M I T N R M
H S S N P O E O Q S
O A L E N W X C D A
A S U A Y A A A I R
T N T O C O S W K I
N A R B H A T U E Z
A K S A N D I E G O
L F D O L G P H J N
T I O R T E D R M A
A I N I G R I V Z N
```

SPRING SEARCH

Find and circle these words about **SPRING**.
They go up, down, forward, backward,
and diagonally.

APRIL

BASEBALL

BICYCLES

EASTER

EQUINOX

FIESTA

GARDEN

MARCH

NATURE

PASSOVER

PROM

SAND

SHADES

SOUTH

SPRING BREAK

TULIPS

SPRING HOLIDAY FUN

```
S  R  E  V  O  S  S  A  P
P  E  Q  M  O  R  P  H  Y
R  T  U  G  A  R  D  E  N
I  S  I  S  I  D  S  A  A
N  A  N  L  I  O  S  S  T
G  E  O  G  U  C  A  E  U
B  O  X  T  R  N  D  L  R
R  H  H  A  D  A  E  C  E
E  J  M  N  A  N  S  Y  W
A  T  U  L  I  P  S  C  Q
K  I  T  A  T  S  E  I  F
L  L  A  B  E  S  A  B  T
```

LOOK ALIKE

THERE ARE **12** THINGS THAT ARE DIFFERENT BETWEEN THIS PICTURE OF *HUMPTY DUMPTY* AND THE ONE ON THE NEXT PAGE. FIND AND CIRCLE THEM.

LANDING MAZE

YOU ARE THE PILOT OF THIS JET!
TRAVEL THROUGH THIS MAZE AND
LAND AT THE AIRPORT.

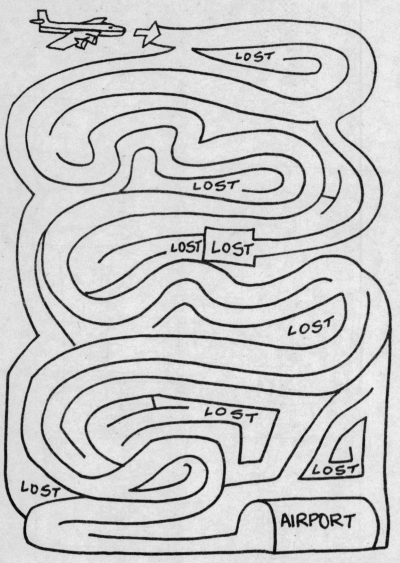

CROSSWORD SCRAMBLE!

Complete this crossword puzzle. Then write the circled letters in the spaces below. On the next page, unscramble the mystery word.

ACROSS:
2- TEN PLUS EIGHT.
4- A FARM ANIMAL.
5- YOU HEAR WITH THESE.

DOWN:
1- OPPOSITE OF RIGHT.
3- PLACE TO KEEP A CAR.

SCRAMBLED LETTERS:

___ ___ ___ ___ ___ ___ ___ ___

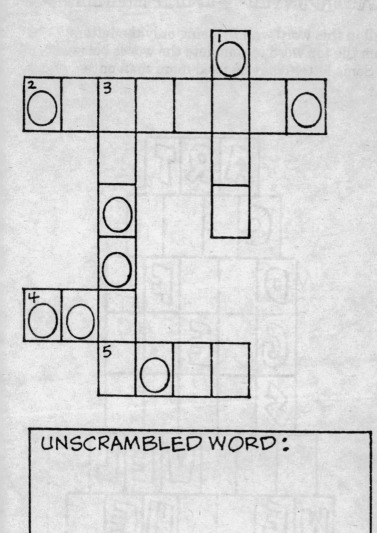

UNSCRAMBLED WORD:

___ ___ ___ ___ ___ ___ ___ ___

WORD WALL

Fill in this word wall by using only the letters from the top word to complete the words below. Some letters may be used more than once.

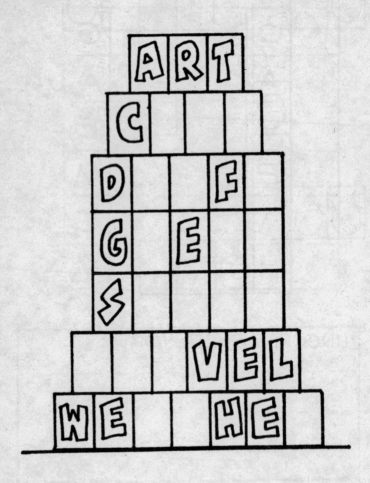

DID YOU KNOW...

CIRCLE ALL THE ODD-NUMBERED LETTERS AND WRITE THEM, AS THEY APPEAR, TO COMPLETE THIS MESSAGE.

4 B	5 C	10 G	3 A	11 N	7 G
9 E	6 A	1 T	13 C	8 F	5 A
2 D	3 V	21 I	19 T	17 I	11 E
1 S	5 F	12 E	3 R	9 O	7 M
11 E	17 A	21 T	5 I	3 N	16 C
1 G	3 H	5 O	7 N	11 E	9 Y

... THAT BEARS

___ ___ ___   ___ ___ ___

___ ___ ___ ___ ___ ___ ___ ___

___ ___ ___ ___

___ ___ ___ ___ ___ ___

___ ___ ___ ___ ___ ?

117

WORD FIND

Find and circle these **CAREER** words. They go up, down, forward, backward, and diagonally.

ACTOR	INVENTOR
ASTRONAUT	MAYOR
CHEF	MUSICIAN
DANCER	NURSE
DOCTOR	PAINTER
FARMER	PLUMBER
LAWYER	RANGER
LIFEGUARD	WRITER

```
D  R  A  U  G  E  F  I  L
R  R  E  T  N  I  A  P  Y
E  L  R  E  Y  W  A  L  T
G  F  T  C  H  E  F  U  U
N  A  I  C  I  S  U  M  A
A  R  E  T  I  R  W  B  N
R  M  K  B  O  U  H  E  O
R  E  R  T  N  M  R  R  R
X  R  C  M  A  Y  O  R  T
R  O  T  N  E  V  N  I  S
D  S  D  S  R  O  T  C  A
D  A  N  C  E  R  T  R  T
```

MYSTERY MESSAGE

Going across, circle every third letter. Write the circled letters, in the order they appear, in the blank spaces below.

H	L	G	Y	K
O	G	H	I	T
N	N	C	Y	G
W	L	T	S	N
O	S	N	W	H
F	O	S	T	R
N	Y	K	T	R

WE'RE

_ _ _ _ _

_ _

_ _ _ _ !

STORMY MAZE

HELP THESE TRICK OR TREATERS TRAVEL
THROUGH THIS TERRIBLE STORM AND
ARRIVE HOME SAFELY!

ON THE LOOKOUT

FIND THE FOLLOWING NUMBERS AND LETTERS HIDDEN IN THIS PICTURE. 1 · 2 · 3 · 4 · 5
A · B · C · D · E

COUNTING

HOW MANY MITTENS
CAN YOU COUNT ?
BE CAREFUL, AS MANY
OVERLAP.

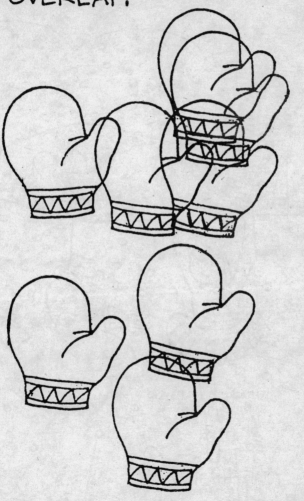

TOTAL _____

DON'T BELONG

FIND AND CIRCLE 6 THINGS THAT
DON'T BELONG IN THIS PICTURE.

KEEP
OFF THE
GRASS

DROP·A·LETTER

Drop a letter from each word in column **A**
to make a new word in column **B**.

Write the dropped letters in the circles
to reveal the mystery word.

A	B	
LINK	INK	Ⓛ
READ		◯
SUIT		◯
SONG		◯
THIN		◯
RAIN		◯
NONE		◯
GATE		◯

8 TINY REINDEER

PLACE THESE NAMES IN THEIR CORRECT SPACES.
BLITZEN • COMET • CUPID •
DANCER • DASHER • DONNER •
PRANCER • VIXEN

	P	R	A	N	C	E	R	

ALL AROUND THE WORLD

Find and circle the names of these countries and continents. They go up, down, forward, backward, and diagonally.

- [ ] AFRICA
- [ ] ASIA
- [ ] AUSTRALIA
- [ ] CHINA
- [ ] EGYPT
- [ ] ENGLAND
- [ ] EUROPE
- [ ] ITALY
- [ ] JAPAN
- [ ] SPAIN
- [ ] U.S.A.

A	I	S	A	R	N	E
I	U	P	Y	D	A	N
L	S	A	L	T	P	G
A	A	I	A	C	A	L
R	O	N	T	C	J	A
T	C	H	I	N	A	N
S	M	R	N	Z	B	D
U	F	E	G	Y	P	T
A	E	P	O	R	U	E

LOOK and FIND

Find and circle these **LOVE** words.
They go up, down, forward, backward,
and diagonally.

ADORE
BOY
CARD
CARE
CUPID
CUTE
DATE
EMOTION
FEBRUARY
FLOWERS

GIFT
GIRL
GIVE
HEART
KIND
KISS
LOVE
SWEET
TOGETHER

```
N  O  I  T  O  M  E  L  H
T  N  Y  E  R  O  D  A  G
E  C  U  T  E  D  N  I  K
V  S  U  S  T  A  V  N  I
O  H  G  F  A  E  F  R  S
L  O  I  L  D  B  E  A  S
D  G  R  O  B  H  B  W  A
I  B  L  W  T  A  R  N  S
P  G  L  E  E  S  U  C  Y
U  Q  G  R  T  R  A  E  H
C  O  A  S  D  R  U  O  I
T  C  A  S  D  R  Y  O  B
```

A FUN FACT

FIND AND CROSS OUT ALL THE **Q** AND **V** LETTERS. WRITE THE REMAINING LETTERS, AS THEY APPEAR, TO READ THIS FACT.

P	Q	O	V	T	Q
V	A	T	O	V	C
H	V	I	Q	P	S
W	E	R	V	E	M
Q	A	D	E	V	B
Y	G	E	Q	O	V
V	R	G	E	C	Q
R	U	M	B	Q	V
Q	V	I	Q	V	N

THE FIRST __ __ __ __ __ __ __

__ __ __ __ __ __ __

__ __ __ __ __ __

__ __ __ __ __ __ __ __

__ __ 1835.

MAZE

FIND...

9 THINGS THAT ARE
DIFFERENT BETWEEN
THESE TWO PICTURES.

MYSTERY MESSAGE

Going across, circle every third letter. Write the circled letters, in the order they appear, in the blank spaces below.

__ __ __ __ __ __ __ __ __

SPOTPIX

SOME SPORTS
HISTORIANS BELIEVE
THAT THE GAME OF
POLO ACTUALLY
BEGAN IN MEDIEVAL
ENGLAND. HERE, A
MEMBER OF KING
ARTHUR'S "YANKEES"
ATTEMPTS TO GAIN
POSSESSION OF
THE BALL. TOO
MANY INJURIES
PUT AN END TO THE
SPORT UNTIL IT WAS
SAFELY REVIVED IN
1862.
CAN YOU FIND ALL
26 LETTERS OF THE
ALPHABET HIDDEN
IN THIS SCENE?

137

SUMMER FIND

Find and circle these words about **SUMMER**.
They go up, down, forward, backward,
and diagonally.

- •AUGUST
- •BARBECUE
- •BEACH
- •CAMP
- •FUN
- •HOT
- •HUMID
- •JULY
- •PLAY
- •POOL
- •SAND
- •SPORTS
- •SUNNY
- •SWIM
- •TRAVEL
- •VACATION

```
B N O I T A C A V
A P M A C J U L Y
R L V F Y G O T N
B A N T U O C V N
E Y O S P N B Z U
C H T R A V E L S
U R J D D N A S W
E H U M I D C D I
S T R O P S H O M
```

MAZE AWARD

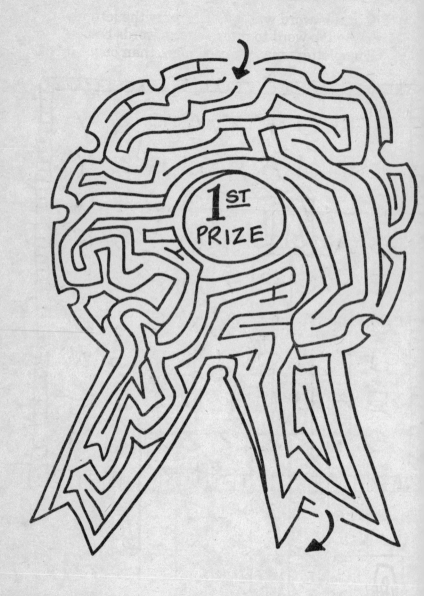

BUILD A WALL

Fill in this word wall by using only the letters
from the top word to complete the words below.
Some letters may be used more than once.

WHAT'S DIFFERENT

CAN YOU FIND AT LEAST 5 THINGS THAT
ARE DIFFERENT BETWEEN THESE TWO
HAUNTED HOUSES?

LOOK AT THIS

FIND AND CIRCLE THESE
HIDDEN PICTURES:
APPLE • CAP • HEART •
IGLOO • SEAL •

COUNT CANES

HOW MANY CANDY CANES DO YOU SEE?
COUNT CAREFULLY AS MANY OVERLAP!

TOTAL: _____

CROSSWORD PIX

SOLVE THIS PICTURE CROSSWORD.
THEN PLACE THE CIRCLED
LETTERS, IN THEIR CORRECT
NUMERICAL ORDER, TO FORM
THE MYSTERY WORD.

_ _ _ _ _ _
1 2 3 4 5 6

SCHOOL MAZE

GET TO SCHOOL ON TIME BY CORRECTLY GOING THROUGH THIS MAZE.

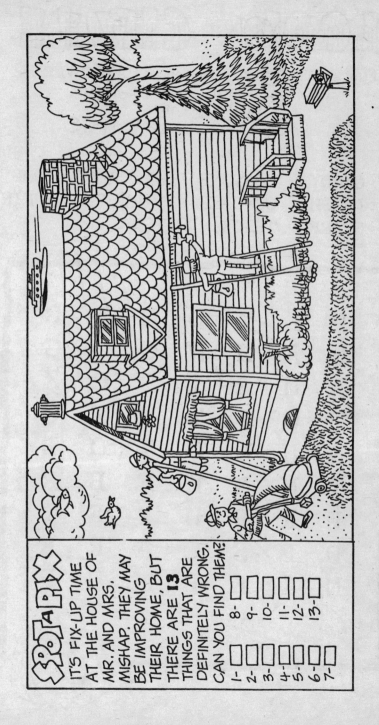

147

LOOK AND CIRCLE

Find and circle these words about **HALLOWEEN**.
They go up, down, forward, backward,
and diagonally.

CANDY   COSTUME   HAUNTED   JUMP
LAUGH   OCTOBER   PARTY   PUMPKIN
SCARE   TRICK   WITCH

```
P  L  Y  D  N  A  C
H  A  Z  W  Q  O  G
A  U  R  I  S  C  K
U  G  J  T  V  T  C
N  H  U  C  Y  O  I
T  M  M  H  F  B  R
E  R  P  U  Y  E  T
D  B  S  C  A  R  E
N  I  K  P  M  U  P
```

SPOTaPIX

THE IDENTICAL FLYING ENCHILADA BROTHERS WERE KNOWN FOR THEIR FLYING MACHINES AND THEIR BEARDS. AFTER A MID AIR COLLISION IN 1898, THEY DECIDED TO SELL BEARD GROOMING KITS. "ONE CANNOT FALL OUT OF THE SKY WHEN BUSY TRIMMING ONE'S BEARD!" THEY ONCE STATED. FIND 10 THINGS THAT ARE DIFFERENT BETWEEN THE TWO BROTHERS.

A HIDDEN MESSAGE FROM

MOM

CROSS OUT ALL THE LETTERS THAT APPEAR **4** TIMES. WRITE THE REMAINING LETTERS, AS THEY APPEAR, IN THE SPACES BELOW.

	W	Q	B		
	K	I	E	E	I
Q	D	P	Y	O	U	W
B	R	R	I	O	O	B
W	M	D	C	D	L	Q
	D	E	A	I	N
	Q	B	W		

___ ___ ___ ___ ___ ___

___ ___ ___ ___

___ ___ ___ ___ ___ !

FILL-IN

Fill in the areas that contain a dot to find out the
temperature at which water freezes
(in degrees Fahrenheit).

WRITE-IN

WRITE THE ANSWER TO
EACH CLUE IN THE BOXES.
IF THEY ARE CORRECT, THE
ANSWERS WILL READ THE
SAME *DOWN* AS THEY DO
ACROSS.

NOT
GOOD...

LARGE
MONKEY...

FAMILY
ROOM...

CROSS-OUT

CROSS OUT THE LETTERS THAT HAVE A TRIANGLE △. WRITE THE REMAINING LETTERS, AS THEY APPEAR, TO REVEAL THE MYSTERY WORDS.

S	C	Y	T
B	A	Q	Y
D	W	F	H
A	E	R	K
I	M	R	U

_ _ _ _ _ _ _ _ !

COUNT T's

HOW MANY TIMES DOES THE LETTER "T" APPEAR IN THIS PICTURE? CIRCLE EACH ONE.

TOTAL: _____

14 KIDS

THE WORD **KIDS** APPEARS
14 TIMES IN THIS PUZZLE.
FIND AND CIRCLE THEM ALL.

```
K  K  S  K  K  D
I  S  D  I  K  S
D  K  I  D  S  S
S  K  K  S  D  K
S  S  I  S  I  I
D  D  D  D  K  D
I  I  S  S  S  S
K  K  I  D  S  S
```

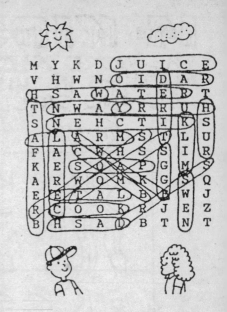

Page 8

Page 9

A N   A N I M A L
WED SUN   WED SUN THURS MON WED FRI
11 22   11 22   5   16 11 20

T H A T
FRI FRI WED FRI
6   13 11 6

S T I N K S   A N D
WED FRI THURS SUN MON WED   WED SUN TUES
4   6   5   22 23 4   11 22 24

S T I N G S !
WED FRI THURS SUN TUES WED
4   6   5   22 17   4

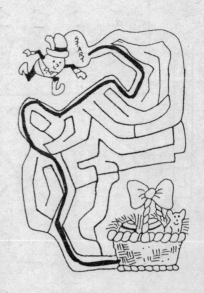

Page 10

Page 11

D O N'T
4 15 14 20

B E
2 5

A
1

L I T T E R
12 9 20 20 5 18

B U G !
2 21 7

Pages 12-13

Pages 14-15

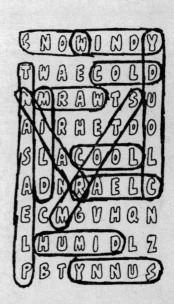

Page 16

TOTAL - 25

Page 17

Page 18

Page 19

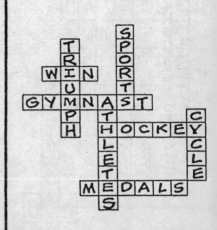

Page 20

B E C A U S E   S H E
H A D   A
P U M P K I N   F O R
A   C O A C H !

Page 21

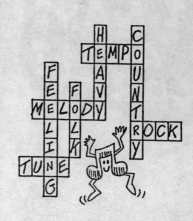

Page 22

T H E   F I R S T
1 10 2   19 7 8 6 1

P U B L I C
25 17 13 15 7 4

S C H O O L   I N
6 4 10 9 9 15   7 16

T H E   U. S.
1 10 2   17 6

O P E N E D   I N
9 25 2 16 2 22   7 16

F E B R U A R Y
19 2 13 6 17 20 8 24

1635.

Page 23

	1-	2-	3-
1-	W	E	T
2-	E	W	E
3-	T	E	N

159

Page 24

Page 25

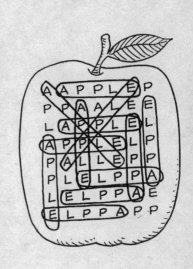

Page 26

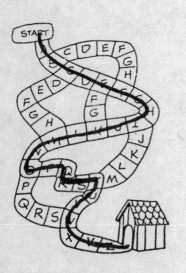

Page 27

DOT   SOFT
DOWN   SON
DROWN   STIR
FIRST   SWIFT
FIST   SWORD
FIT   TIN
FOR   TON
FRONT   TOWN
NO   WIN
NOD   WON
OWN   WORD
RID   WORN
RIOT
ROD   — ARE A
ROT   FEW OF
ROW   THE WORDS
SIFT   YOU CAN
SIN   MAKE.

LOOK OUT FOR SCARY GOBLINS!

Page 32

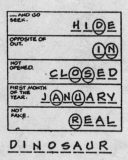

Page 33

Page 34

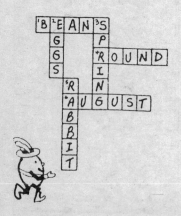

Page 35

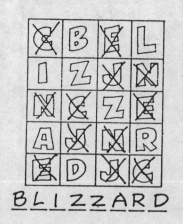

BLIZZARD

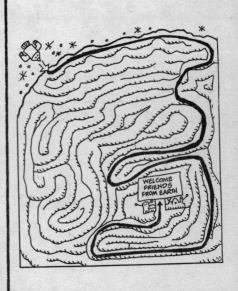

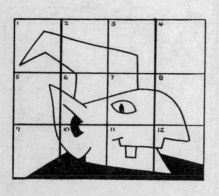

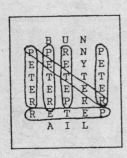

BUNNY TRAIL

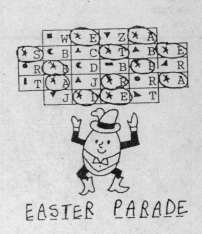

EASTER PARADE

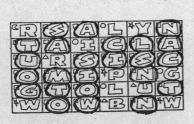

SANTA CLAUS
IS COMING
TO TOWN.

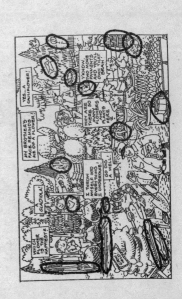

Page 48

Here are only some of the words you can make from: WELCOME BACK!

bake	block	claw	lake	mole
balm	bowl	cloak	law	wake
beam	cab	clock	lock	web
become	cake	comb	mob	
black	calm	lack	mock	

Page 49

Pages 50-51

Pages 52-53

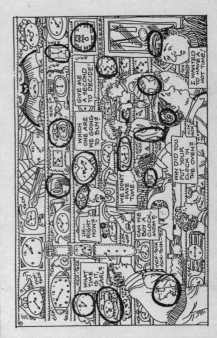

Pages 56-57

Here are only some of the words you can make from: SUPERCALIFRAGILISTIC

accuse	lisp
acute	pea
case	rag
cause	real
crate	ripe
cusp	sag
cute	scale
face	scarf
fall	sea
far	sell
farce	slate
fist	slice
flip	slip
flute	spell
fuse	sugar
gas	super
grill	tar
ice	tell
icicle	trip
large	use

Pages 58-59

Page 60

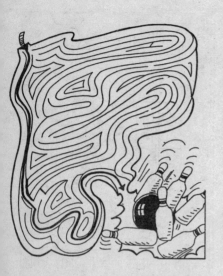

Page 61

A TICKLE
IN YOUR
THROAT!

Pages 62-63

THANKSGIVING

BASEBALL

GREAT

BABE RUTH

WAS BORN

FEBRUARY

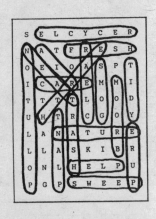

YOU CAN PREVENT NOISE POLLUTION
STOP TALKING.

CROCODILE

18TH PRESIDENT

ULYSSES S.

TNARG
GRANT

32ND PRESIDENT

FRANKLIN D.

OROSEVTLE
ROOSEVELT

Page 74

Page 75

Page 76

1-H	10-A
2-E	11-D
3-L	12-O
4-U	13-C
5-D	14-N
6-R	15-E
7-B	16-S
8-L	17-K
9-T	18-W

B E C A U S E
7 2 13 10 4 16 2

S H E
16 1 15

W A N T E D
18 10 14 9 2 5

T O
9 12

R O C K
6 12 13 17

A N D
10 14 11

R O L L !
6 12 3 8

Page 77

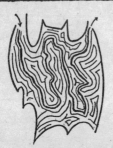

Page 78

Here are only some of the words
you can make from: SPIDERWEB

bed	ripe
bee	rise
beep	see
bid	seed
birds	seep
brew	sew
bride	sip
deer	spew
dew	spire
dip	weed
peer	weep
pie	wide
pride	wipe
red	wire
ribs	wise
ride	wisp
rip	

171

Page 79

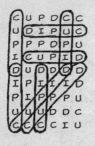

Page 80

WE'RE GOING TO
T H E
M O V I E S !

Page 82

OPPOSITE OF
FIRST   (L) A S T

YOU HAVE 5 OF THESE ON
EACH HAND   F (I) N G E R S

FROZEN
WATER   I (C) E

HALLOWEEN
MONTH   (O) C T O B E R

YELLOW CITRUS
FRUIT   (L) E M O (N)

L I N C O L N
MYSTERY NAME

Page 83

172

Page 84

Page 85

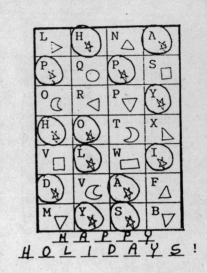

H A P P Y

H O L I D A Y S !

Page 86

OPPOSITE OF HOT – ©O L D

THIRD MONTH OF THE YEAR – M A R C H

SMALL POOL OF RAIN – P U D D L E

THIRD DAY OF THE WEEK – T U E S D A Y

NOT SQUARE – R O U N D

C O M P U T E R

MYSTERY WORD

Page 87

OPEN	(NOT CLOSED)
APPLE	(A JUICY RED FRUIT)
SHOE	(YOU WEAR THIS ON YOUR FOOT)
UMBRELLA	(OPEN THIS UP WHEN IT RAINS)
WINTER	(DECEMBER TO MARCH)
PIANO	(EIGHTY-EIGHT KEYS)
NOVEMBER	(THANKSGIVING MONTH)

173

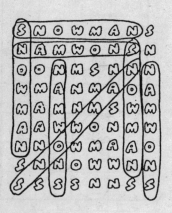

DON'T BE A LITTERBUG!

1) ETHRA	HEART	
2) EOVL	LOVE	
3) CPDUI	CUPID	
4) KSIS	KISS	
5) FEOWLSR	FLOWERS	
6) VGIE	GIVE	

174

TOTAL _7_

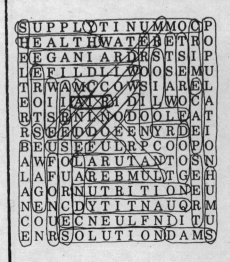

Pages 96-97

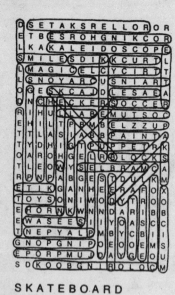

SKATEBOARD

Pages 98-99

Page 100

Page 101

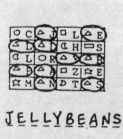

JELLYBEANS

176

Page 102

I T'S
FUN
TO
BUILD
CASTLES
IN
THE
SNOW.

Page 103

SHOOT A 3-POINT BASKET.

Pages 104-105

Pages 106-107

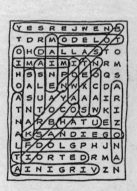

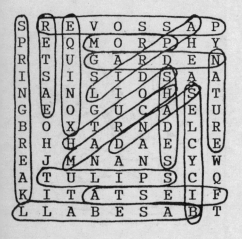

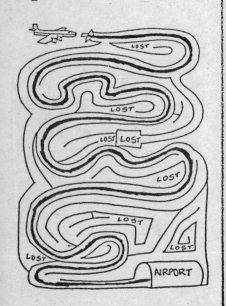

Pages 114-115

UNSCRAMBLED WORD:

AIRPLANE

Page 116

Page 117

...THAT BEARS
CAN GET
CAVITIES
FROM
EATING
HONEY?

Pages 118-119

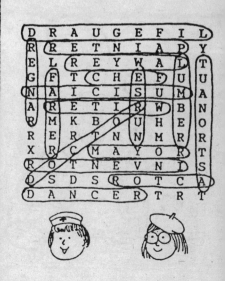

179

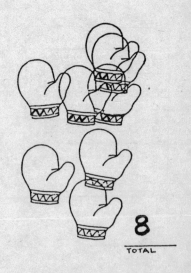

Page 126

A	B	
LINK	INK	L
READ	RED	A
SUIT	SIT	U
SONG	SON	G
THIN	TIN	H
RAIN	RAN	I
NONE	ONE	N
GATE	ATE	G

Page 127

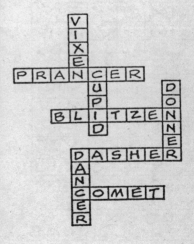

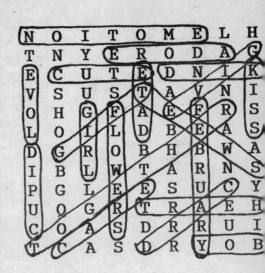

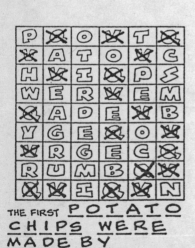

THE FIRST POTATO CHIPS WERE MADE BY GEORGE CRUMB IN 1835.

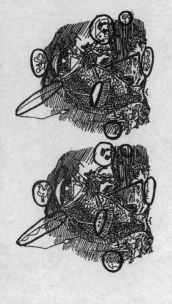

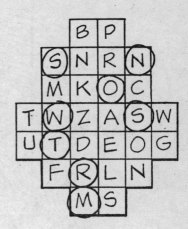

SNOWSTORM

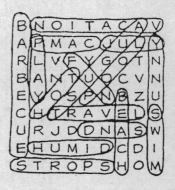

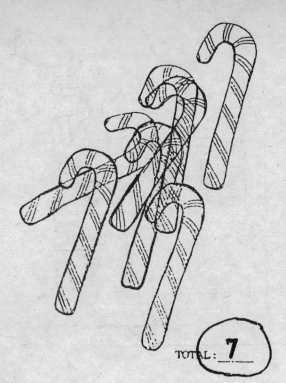

TOTAL : __7__

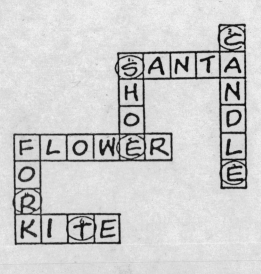

S E C R E T
1 2 3 4 5 6

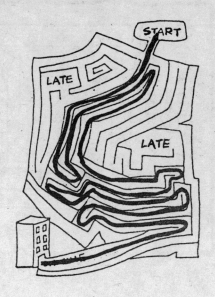

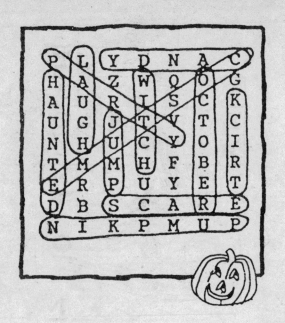

KEEP YOUR
ROOM
CLEAN!

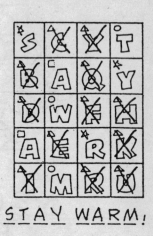

S T A Y   W A R M !

TOTAL: 7

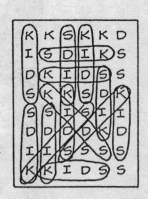

How to get *even MORE*

AWESOME
ACTIVITIES

Pick up a pencil and plunge right in to the most awesome activities around. You'll find word searches, crosswords, mazes, hidden pictures, secret codes, mystery pictures to draw and **more**. Once you have one book, you'll want to collect them all!

Each book is
ONLY $2.50
plus $1.00 for
postage and handling.

— — — — — — — — — — — — — — — — — — — —

Send check or money order and coupon to:
KIDSBOOKS, INC.
3535 W. Peterson Ave.
Chicago, IL 60659

Enclosed is $_____ for _____ book(s) which includes postage and handling charges. (No COD's)

Check quantity for each:

____#1	____#4	____#7	____#10	____#13	____#16
____#2	____#5	____#8	____#11	____#14	____#17
____#3	____#6	____#9	____#12	____#15	____#18

Name_____

Address_____

City_____**State**_____**Zip**_____

Offer good for U.S. residents only.
Please allow 4-6 weeks for delivery.
Residents of Illinois please add the appropriate state and local sales tax.